DOUBLE TAKE

HONOR #1

PROTECT. SERVE.
BEAT. BURN.

$2.50

ORTEGA | JEMAS | ROWE | RODRIGUEZ

ULTIMATE TECHNOLOGY
Buyer's Guide

YOUR GUIDE TO THE BEST, TELEPHONES, TV'S, CAMERA'S, AND COMPUTERS **PLUS** A SNEAK PEEK AT THE SMARTEST CAR IN TOWN.

HONDA S-600

The smartest car in town for the family that has the latest high technology in their home. This car is smart in style with power to spare. It's easy to handle, easy to park and has spacious luggage compartment for family trips.

$6500; at your local Honda dealership

MOTOROLA POCKET RADIO

A shirt-pocket radio with the power and sound you'd expect from a larger set. A 6-transistor chassis pinpoints stations and the speaker delivers sound in rich, clear lows and crisp highs. With battery life up to 100 hours, you can take it on a trip in a custom carrying case.

$14; mail order

AT&T PRINCESS PHONE

America has fallen in love with the new Princess phone. It's little so it fits in those small places where you couldn't fit a telephone before. It's lovely and charms people with its graceful lines and color. It lights so you can find it easily in the dark.

$35; mail order

RCA COLOR TELEVISION

In living color. Get a perfectly fine-tuned picture with brighter highlights every time you watch and circuitry that won't go haywire.

$55; Kaufmann's

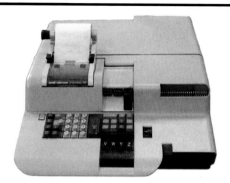

OLIVETTI PROGRAMMA 101

The first computer on your desk. Every company, university, department, laboratory or institute can now have their own private electronic digital computer. It's only a little larger than a typewriter and doesn't require a skilled operator.

$75; mail order

STORY
BILL JEMAS
JULIAN ROWE

SCRIPT
FRANK ORTEGA
BILL JEMAS

LAYOUTS
JULIAN ROWE

PENCILS
CARLOS RODRIGUEZ

COLORS
PETER PANTAZIS

COVER
APPLE QINGYANG ZHANG

LETTERS
CHAROLOTTE GREENBAUM

EDITOR
CHARLOTTE GREENBAUM

DOUBLE TAKE

RICHARD BROOKS | PRODUCTION ASSISTANT

MICHAEL COAST | STORY EDITOR

CLAIRE DRANGINIS | PRODUCTION COORDINATOR

CAROLINE FLANAGAN | PRODUCTION ASSISTANT

ALLISON GADSDEN | EDITORIAL INTERN

WILLIAM GRAVES | DIGITAL PRODUCTION ARTIST

CHARLOTTE GREENBAUM | EDITORIAL ASSISTANT

YOUNG HELLER | STORYBOARD ILLUSTRATOR

BILL JEMAS | GENERAL MANAGER

ELYSIA LIANG | EDITORIAL ASSISTANT

ROBERT MEYERS | MANAGING EDITOR

JULIAN ROWE | STORYBOARD ILLUSTRATOR

LILLIAN TAN | BUSINESS MANAGER

GABE YOCUM | SALES & MARKETING COORDINATOR

Honor #1. September 2015. Published by Double Take, LLC, a subsidiary of Take-Two Interactive Software, Inc. Office of publication: 38 W. 39 Street, 2nd Floor, New York, NY 10018. ©2015 Take-Two Interactive Software, Inc. All Rights Reserved. Printed in Canada.

DISCOVER THE LARGEST INDEPENDENT SUPERHERO UNIVERSE
IN COMICS | EACH VOLUME ONE ONLY $9.99

Can you survive the zombie apocalypse?

Yes? You probably think you can.
There is only one way to find out.

Play the **Dead Reign® RPG**. The core rule book, a few players, some dice and an active imagination are all you need to start playing. Rules are easy. Character creation is fast and fun. Combat, quick and deadly. Survival? Harder than you may think.

• **7 different types of zombies. Zombie combat and survival tips.**

• **6 Apocalyptic Character Classes and Ordinary People.**

• **101 Random Scenarios, Encounters, Settings and places of note.**

• **100 Random Corpse Searches, other tables, weapons & vehicles.**

• **Death Cults, their Priests, power over zombies and goals.**

• **Quick Roll Character Creation tables (10 minutes).**

• **5 sourcebooks provide more types of zombies, survival tips, new dangers and adventure.**

• **The Dead Reign™ core rule book is 224 pages – Cat. No. 230. A complete role-playing game book.**

Discover the Palladium Books® RPG Megaverse®

Fun to read. A blast to play. The Palladium role-playing rule system is the same in every game. This means once readers become familiar with one game, they can play them *ALL*.

Better yet, you can link and combine several game worlds to create epic, multi-dimensional adventures on a cosmic scale!

What's that? You've never seen a role-playing game? The role-playing core rule book contains all the rules and data you need to create characters and get you started. Each game or supplement is a magazine size soft-bound or hardcover book, 48-352 pages, and jam-packed with great art, heroes, villains, adventures and tons of ideas. **Dead Reign®** and **Robotech®** are excellent for those of you new to pen and paper RPGs.

Rifts® is the Earth of the future, but a transformed and alien Earth where magic and technology coexist and realities from countless dimensions collide. Alien predators and supernatural monsters prey upon the human survivors and threaten to conquer the world.

Players can be any number of aliens, mutants, warriors, cyborgs, robots and wizards. Lines of magic crisscross the Earth, giving life to dragons, godlings and supernatural horrors. They also lead to dimensional gateways called "Rifts" that link the Earth to the infinite Megaverse®. In **Rifts®** anything is possible.

Unleash your imagination! Drop by our website to learn more about our games or make purchases from our online store. Also available in comic book and game stores everywhere.

www.palladiumbooks.com

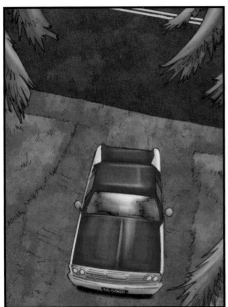

Dispatch. Urgent. I need an ambulance out here on Route 17, near mile marker 35. Car accident. Three severely wounded.

Call Stu, get his hook out here.

Right, Chief.

EVOLVE

CHOOSE YOUR SIDE

Chief, we'll come back for Freddy's body.

We left a bag, if you're up to it.

Rest easy buddy. I'll make sure you get your blue ribbon.

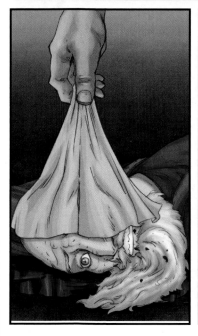

The war to end all wars.

DOUBLE TAKE

HONOR #2

DEAD BADGE
OF COURAGE

NEXT ISSUE

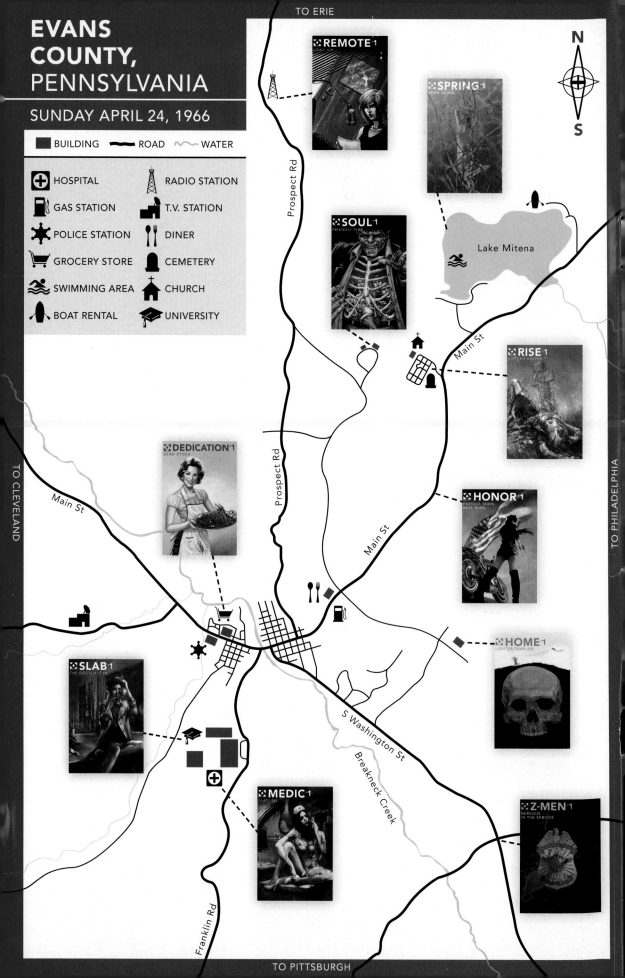